WILTON - THE FIRST FIFTY YEARS

ACKNOWLEDGMENTS

It is not the aim of this book to provide a comprehensive and detailed history of the Teesside-based chemical production complex formerly known as the Wilton Works, but rather to illustrate, with a selection of photographs taken over the last 50 years, some of the chemical plants and people involved in making Wilton the unique place that it is, and hopefully rekindling many happy memories of times and lifestyles which probably will not be repeated.

It is appreciated that, sadly, many of the people pictured are no longer with us, however no distress is intended towards their friends and relatives, but hopefully this book will provide a tribute to the part they played in Wilton's first 50 years.

Thanks to all who helped in this production, especially Roy Billany, Bill Perfitt, Terry Waldron, Bob Wasson, Kath McPartland, Pauline McMaster, June Hurworth and all the photographers responsible for the historical pictures, together with Marc Thorneycroft and Paul Martin of The PhotoWorks, Wilton, for the more recent material.

WILTON - THE FIRST FIFTY YEARS

Designed and produced by C.J. Hurworth

Printed and published by Falcon Press (Stockton-on-Tees Ltd), Stockton on Tees. TS18 2ES

This edition copyright 1999
ISBN 1 - 872339 - 01- 8

WILTON - THE FIRST FIFTY YEARS

Compiled by
Colin Hurworth

FOREWORD
by Sir John Harvey-Jones, MBE

"I feel very honoured to have been invited to write the foreword
for this splendid commemorative book, although I fear my contribution to
Wilton over the years does not really justify this honour.

However, I can say with total honesty that Wilton, my friends there and
the values and beliefs of the whole organisation were really the bedrock of
all my subsequent thinking and actions in the field of industry.

Like everybody else who was there at the time, I firmly believe that I was
privileged to be a part of the building of Britain's industrial future.

A future based not only on technology, but also on respect for individuals
and real concern for the people involved in the production processes, as
well as commitment to the environment.

I joined this mighty endeavour in 1957, straight from a career in the armed
services, and was totally amazed at the decency and values which were
expressed in the behaviour and beliefs of every single one of us, from the
Chairman right down to the newest member of the shop floor.

Looking back on it I feel that my introduction to ICI was a particularly
fortunate one, as I joined as a Work Study Officer. I therefore spent my
first three years working closely with many people who, at that time, were
working on the shop floor in the shift system.

I remember being greatly impressed by the general calibre and wide range
of interests of the workers and many of the people I worked with in the
early days proved to be good friends over the years.

Those of us who toiled at that time have every reason to be proud of what
we achieved.

We accomplished so much by working together in a group with, almost, a single purpose.

Moreover we placed great importance on the newest developments in technology, the newest thinking in terms of man-management and the newest ideas in terms of health and safety and the environment. We were truly at the leading edge.

I am delighted at the typically 'Wiltonian' initiative of printing this book and hope and believe that it will give as much pleasure to all my friends and colleagues, past and present, as it has to me."

Sir John Harvey-Jones MBE

In July 1949 the Plastics Division of ICI pioneered the first operational plant on the Wilton Site.

This was the unit for manufacturing phenolic moulding powder - the PF Plant as it became known, and was followed very closely by the opening of the Perspex Plant in August.

The PF Plant in 1949, - the first operational production unit on the Wilton Site.

So began the unique chemical production complex, which over the next 50 years has produced inestimable millions of tons of countless diverse chemicals and provided a unique way of life to many, many thousands of workers and their families.

The story, however, begins a few years earlier, when in May 1945, ICI announced its intention to establish a new factory on the south bank of the River Tees.

As early as 1943, ICI had begun to make plans for the post-war expansion of its manufacturing facilities. The existing works did not have enough space for all the new plants which were likely to be required, and the idea was conceived of a new composite factory at which any ICI Division could erect plants, many of them inter-related, offering all the savings inherent in siting them together and utilising large scale central services.

Many people believed that the human and organisational problems would be too formidable to overcome, and in fact similar ideas in the United States had already been rejected by the chemical industry. However, ICI made its mind up to go ahead, probably thanks to the efforts of Sir Holbrook Gaskell, and Mr W. F. Lutyens, ICI Board members during the war years.

In June 1945, the "Site X" team began assembling at temporary headquarters, 88 High Street, Norton, and in December announced the purchase of the Wilton Site.

Work began very rapidly after the announcement. In January 1946 the first staff occupied Wilton Castle, and the adjacent huts, formerly a military hospital, became the design offices.

The first major contractor, J. B. Edwards of London, with a five year contract for roads and drains, began work in April 1946 on the first site road - the north end of what is now Queens Avenue.

Early construction work by J.B. Edwards of the North South Road, looking North from Piccadilly Roundabout.

Excavation work in progress for the foundations of the Perspex Building.
Looking West, to the area later occupied by Nylon Works.

To co-ordinate the policy on the site, a group of resident senior executives was required, and therefore a Chairman, Managing Director, Technical Director, Engineering Director, Director and Chief Accountant, Works and Personnel Director, and Secretary were soon appointed.

Together with the Chairman of each of the operating Divisions, so was formed the controlling authority for Wilton Works, responding only to the ICI Board.

The foundations and original layout of Wilton were the responsibility of

Dr. J.W. Armitt, the first Chairman of the Wilton Council, a man who firmly believed in the importance of a leisure time meeting place at Wilton, so that people could play as well as work together. His close interest in the Wilton Works Recreation Club and its activities set a tradition kept up by his successors for many years.

Sir Ewart Smith was given the task of setting up the structure of Wilton within ICI's overall organisation, and together with Sir Alexander Fleck, the Group Director with responsibility for Wilton, provided much help and guidance during the early years.

The Inaugural Meeting of the Wilton Council, 7th November 1946

Back Row :   F. Potter, W.H. Demuth, W.O. Wright, W.J. Worboys, H.S. Hirst, A.A. Swinbank.
Front Row: J.W. McDavid, V. St. J. Killery, J.W. Armitt (Chairman), K. Gordon, W.M. Inman.
Not on photograph: N.D. Lees.

General view, looking North West from the top of the Meteorological Station at Wilton Grange.
The North-South Road and Main Stores are under construction.

The construction work was pushed forward at a remarkable rate, particularly when you consider that in 1945 Wilton was just a peaceful agricultural scene. There were many difficulties and shortages of all kinds in those post-war years, plus the fact that men were returning from active service to settle down in civilian life.

By September 1947, the first permanent building, the Apprentice Training School, next to Piccadilly Circus, was completed and occupied.

In November, the first boiler, the Dalbeatie was in operation, and even Long Service Awards were presented.

In December 1947, the Wilton Works Recreation Club was founded, and the initial occupation of Main Stores took place.

Within the next few years more than £100 million of development was well underway involving a construction labour force of between 2000-5000, of which approximately 1000 were directly employed by ICI, the rest being contractors.

All construction was co-ordinated by the Wilton Engineering Department, with much of the work being carried out by major contractors such as Monk, Laing, Wimpey, and the previously mentioned J.B.Edwards.

In addition to the major contractors there were a host of smaller firms involved, one of which, E.D.Williams of Runcorn was engaged in painting contracts right from the start.

In the Power Station, Babcock & Wilcox and Metropolitan Vickers built the boilers and generating plant, most of the steelwork coming from South Durham, and the pipework from Aiton's. Two local firms, Dorman Long and Redpath Brown supplied additional steelwork.

The plants themselves were built with the assistance of firms such as Matthew Hall, Ashmore Benson, John Brown, together with American companies - Kellogg's and Badger's.

In March 1948 the main workshops were in operation, and the tunnel under the Tees was completed in November.

By 1949, Piccadilly Restaurant had opened, an incentive scheme was introduced, and the number of ICI employees at Wilton had exceeded 1000.

The tunnel under the River Tees.
The tunnelling machinery, originally used for construction of the London Underground system, was supplied on loan to ICI.

First stages of construction of the Main Power Station. Note the area marked out for the first chimney.
Piccadilly Restaurant, the original Apprentice Training School and Main Workshops are in the background.

The official opening took place on September 14th 1949, two months after the first plant became operational.

Lord McGowan, Chairman of ICI marked the historic occasion with the planting of a tree in the area south of Piccadilly Restaurant, which for many years remained as the Piccadilly Rose Garden.

In his speech at the tree planting ceremony, Lord McGowan declared: 'What we propose doing on this site certainly shows initiative and imagination, and confidence in the future'.

Some headlines from the local newspapers are still relevant fifty years on.

Towards the end of 1949, the I.P. Boilers came into full operation and construction work continued at a great pace into the next decade.

By August 1951, No. 1 Olefines Plant was in production, followed in November by No. 1 Polythene. In December the first Wilton Recreation Clubhouse was opened, and the Ethylene Oxide and Ethylene Glycol Plants were commissioned.

In March 1952 the main Power Station was operational, a permanent East Gate was opened in July, and by September the UF/WF Plant was completed.

Construction continued into 1953, hampered only by the terrible East Coast floods which occurred in the January. Part of the sea wall on the tipping area by the river was breached, and there was flooding almost to the railway bridge.

A night and day watch was maintained on the walls, and gangs were kept at the ready to plug any breaches with sandbags.

The UF/WF (Urea Formaldehyde/Woodflour) **Plant**

In January 1954 the Chlorine Plant of Bain Works was in production, and by July there were over 5000 ICI employees on the site. The year ended with Terylene No. 1 plant in full operation.

1955 saw the Titanium Plant and No. 1 Paraxylene Plant being completed, and Polythene became the first works to reach 500,000 hours without a Lost Time Accident.

The Titanium Plant.

In January 1956, ten years after the first staff had arrived on the Wilton Site, the first one million hours without a Lost Time Accident was achieved by the whole site.

Polythene and Olefine Works, looking North East from the Power Station.
Shown also is the Lime Handling Plant (far left), No.1 Process Offices (near left), and part of the Metallurgical Testing Station (right).

On Monday, 4th of June 1956, probably the most memorable visit in the history of the Wilton Site took place, with the arrival of H.M. Queen Elizabeth II and H.R.H. the Duke of Edinburgh, as part of a royal tour of Teesside.

At Wilton, the focal point of the visit was Terylene Works.

After the visit, Central Avenue was re-named Queen's Avenue to commemorate the event.

The Queen being shown a bale of Terylene staple fibre by Sir Alexander Fleck and Dr. A. Caress.

The grandstand built outside the Terylene Plant.
The lady in white at the entrance was handing out Union Jacks to the children.

The West Gate Arch, specially created for the visit.

The Duke of Edinburgh shakes hands with Mr. Scott.

The Royal Car at Piccadilly Roundabout.
To line the route, approximately 17,000 employees and families were brought onto the site, using a fleet of buses, hired from all over Teesside. 10,000 small Union Jacks were purchased, to be waved by the children.

During the first half of 1957 the West Gate came into use, Workshops became the first works to achieve one million hours LTA free, the Labour and Medical Block was opened, and the first large scale polymerisation began on the Butakon Plant.

In October, after one of the greatest successes of construction, Nylon Works began production. The work of no fewer than 49 different contractors was co-ordinated over a site of 60 acres, and yet was completed within 120 weeks.

By the end of the year, No. 5 Boiler, the largest on an industrial site in the UK was in operation, and capital expenditure for the year had reached a record £16,836,000.

1958 began with the formation of the Heavy Organic Chemicals (HOC) Division, and Polythene Works became part of Plastics Division.

In April, the new Apprentice Training Centre was opened by Sir Ewart Smith.

The first issue of the works newspaper, the Wilton News appeared in May, and the scheme for payment of wages by bank credit was introduced.

This was a fine example of the consultation process available at the time, the idea being first raised at the Bain Works Council by Vic Goodsell, then via the Wilton Site Council to the Central Council where it was adopted by the Main Board as an experimental scheme.

By the end of the year there were over 10,000 ICI employees at Wilton, and to increase the sporting facilities available, the gymnasium was opened at the Recreation Club.

The severe drought conditions in the summer of 1959 led to drastic conservation of water to ensure adequate supply to meet the needs of the production plants, and in September, No. 3 Olefines Plant was commissioned.

First Signs of Nylon Works.
Taken from the Perspex Plant, showing the old railway line that ran around the site and into the Main Workshops and Stores.

As Wilton moved into the sixties, a look at the six ICI Divisions operating plants on the site illustrates the efficient integration of the various processes.

Heavy Organic Chemicals.

Three Olefine Plants formed the heart of the Wilton Works. From a single material - naphtha, discharged from ocean-going tankers at Teesport and pumped to Wilton, many of the raw materials for other Wilton Plants were produced.

The two basic processes of thermal cracking and gas separation supplied the primary products - ethylene and propylene of high purity, 'tail gas' consisting of hydrogen and methane, butylenes and butadiene, liquid hydrocarbons (later converted into premium petrol) and fuel oil.

Most of the ethylene was fed to Plastics Division to make 'Alkathene' grade polythene, with the remainder converted to ethylene oxide by the chlorhydrin route. Part of the propylene was piped to Billingham for further processing, with some of the remainder being used to produce 'Propathene' grade polypropylene. The butadiene formed the raw material for the 'Butakon' range of synthetic rubbers and co-polymers.

The other gases were piped to Billingham for further conversion.

The Oxide Plant took ethylene and propylene from the Olefines Plants, chlorine from the

Wilton Chlorine Plant, and lime from Buxton and manufactured ethylene oxide and propylene oxide, with the former being used in the 'Lissapol N' Plant, and for conversion into ethylene glycol.

No.3 Olefines Plant

The Glycol Plants converted the ethylene and propylene oxides into ethylene and propylene glycol. Some of the ethylene glycol was sent for anti-freeze in the motor industry, but most was pumped to the 'Terylene' Plant.

The Butadiene Plant extracted the product from one of the hydrocarbon fractions from the Olefines plants to supply the Butakon Plant with its main raw material. The remaining product was dispatched by sea and road to synthetic rubber manufacturers.

Finally, the Paraxylene Plants, separated the imported xylenes to yield paraxylene, a raw material for the 'Terylene' process. The by-products were sold as aromatic solvents.

Billingham Division

The Formaldehyde Plant took methanol from Billingham and manufactured formaldehyde which was used in Plastic's Division Urea Formaldehyde Moulding Powder Plant, as well as for external sale.

The Formaldehyde Plant

Dyestuffs Division

The Nylon Plant produced nylon, a synthetic material derived from coal, air and water. Synthesis of the basic raw material, coal tar benzene, produced the two key intermediates, adipic acid and hexamethylene diamine. They were converted into nylon polymer, most of which was sent to British Nylon Spinners Ltd for spinning into yarn and staple fibre. Some was also used by Plastics Division for manufacture into 'Maranyl' compounds.

The Phthalic Anhydride Plant produced an important intermediate by catalytic oxidation of naphthalene which was widely used in the manufacture of plasticisers, synthetic resins, paints, dyestuffs, pharmaceuticals and perfumery chemicals.

The Alpha-Naphthylamine Plant, using nitric acid from Billingham, and chlorine from Wilton manufactured a constituent of many dyestuffs and rubber chemicals.

The product of the 'Lissapol N' Plant was used as a wetting and emulsifying agent and also a domestic and industrial detergent by combining ethylene oxide from Wilton with an alkyl phenol from Billingham.

General Chemicals Division

Chlorine, one of the basic heavy chemicals of industry was manufactured by the electrolysis of brine. Some of the chlorine was sold, and the remainder fed to the Ethylene Oxide Plant. In addition to chlorine, the electrolysis process produced caustic soda and hydrogen, most of the soda being sold, and the hydrogen distributed to various Wilton plants.

Using the interaction of titanium tetrachloride and sodium, the Titanium Plant created the strong light metal, whose alloys were so important to the aircraft industry.

General View of Bain Works from the Power Station

Plastics Division

The Polythene Plants produced one of the most important plastics materials in the world. Discovered by scientists at Alkali Division in 1933, the high pressure process used ethylene piped from the Olefines Plants, and was marketed under the 'Alkathene' trade name. About 100,000 tons per year were manufactured for the moulding of housewares, insulation of underwater cables, packaging and other industrial uses.

Methyl methacrylate monomer from Billingham was used on the Perspex Plant to make the acrylic sheet so familiar in signs, baths, sinks, lighting and many other functional and decorative applications.

On the Urea-Formaldehyde Moulding Powder Plant, using urea from Billingham and formaldehyde from Wilton two classes of powder were produced- 'Mouldrite' UF which was paper filled, and 'Mouldrite' WF which was wood-flour filled. These moulding powders were the raw materials from which articles such as radio cabinets, lampshades and kitchenware could be produced in light and attractive colours.

Butadiene, from the plant at Wilton was processed into a range of co-polymers with styrene, acrylonitrile and methyl methacrylate to make 'Butakon' S - used for shoe soleing material, 'Butakon' A for flexible fuel tanks and oil-resistant hoses and 'Butakon' lattices used for leather finishing, coating of printing papers and in the textile industry.

The Propathene Plant took propylene from the Olefines plants and manufactured polypropylene, a new plastic introduced by ICI in 1959 which featured greater rigidity and higher temperature resistance than earlier products, and showed great potential for the future of general extrusion and film forming.

No.1 Propathene Plant

Fibres Division

The synthesis of ethylene glycol and paraxylene, both produced at Wilton created the 'Terylene' polymer from which the fibre of the same name was manufactured. By 1961 the plant produced some 50 million lb. of product per year, used in many applications, both in industry and the home.

The 'Terylene' fibre was manufactured in two forms - a silk-like filament yarn used for dresses, shirts, ties, lingerie and a wool-like staple fibre for suitings, underwear, skirts and socks.

An increasing share of the output was used for industrial applications such as filter-cloths, hose, tyre cords, ropes and threads.

Wilton Castle

The first mention of the existence of a building on the estate seems to have been towards the end of the 11th century when the Bulmer family constructed a wooden manor house.

In 1210, King John granted permission to fortify the house, and by 1331, a license was obtained from King Edward III to convert the manor house to a castle.

The Bulmer connection continued until the mid 16th century when the castle came into the possession of Sir Thomas Cornwallis, and then through his son, grandson and finally to his great grandson Lord Charles Cornwallis in 1698.

In the early 1700's the estate was sold to Sir Stephen Fox, but his son the Earl of Ilchester sold it in 1748 to the trustees of the will of Robert Lowther for the benefit of Sir James Lowther.

By the end of the 18th century the condition of the castle had seriously deteriorated, and following further damage in the storm of 1797 was described in 1805 as being largely a ruin.

Only the discovery of iron ore in the Cleveland Hills and the subsequent wealth generated to the Lowthers enabled the rebuilding and restoration of the castle to be completed.

An artists distorted impression of the Castle , (c.1820), looking North towards the Tees. Reputedly there were three mouths to the river - two narrow ones, and a very wide one as illustrated.

Late 19th Century view showing the old octagonal tower on the right, before the new East Wing/Ballroom was built in 1887.

Between 1810 and 1855 a complete new village was built, out of view of the front of the castle, and the main road (now the A174) was moved away from the castle behind a screen of trees.

The rebuilding of the castle went through three stages. In the first of these, the centre block and West wing were built much as they are now, with a short low East wing. The second stage added a large octagonal tower at the end of the East wing, whilst the third demolished the whole of the wing and replaced it with the present ballroom, guest sitting room and library. The last alteration was finished in 1888 - the date being inscribed over the fireplace.

No recognisable part of the building of 1210 now remains, but the wall in the middle of the studio suite, and that to the East of the entrance are exceptionally thick, and it is possible that they formed part of the original central tower.

The castle continued to be a private residence of the Lowther family until 1945, when

Colonel Lowther agreed to sell the land required by ICI on the condition that they took not only the 2000 acres on the river plain, but a similar area to the south, over the hills towards Guisborough, and also Wilton Castle itself.

Although ICI did not really want the extra land, they did agree to take over the whole estate, and using experienced agricultural colleagues at Billingham, changed the wild moorland of the hilltops into farmland by putting pigs on the land. These rooted out the brambles, bracken and other weeds, making it eventually suitable for sowing. Cattle and sheep are now reared on the pasture, and timber harvested on the steeper hillsides.

The castle and surroundings were used for a variety of purposes, until 1970, when following extensive internal alterations it took on its present use, that of a guest house.

During 1999, ICI decided to put the Castle and grounds up for sale, and at the time of going to press it was unclear what the future plans for Wilton Castle would be.

The castle, in 1946 after many years of neglect. Note the ivy still on the walls, this was later removed.

By 1948 the lawns and flower beds looked a lot tidier.

The Ballroom, before redecoration.
The sheets protected the gold coloured silk wall coverings. The Castle Library - later the Wilton Council Room, then Castle Club Bar, can be seen through the open door.

Aerial view of the Castle, showing the Engineering Huts, Restaurant and Golf Club.
Some of the huts were previously used as a military hospital, and early ICI occupants were subjected to a very strong smell of disinfectant.
The route of the old flint road went in a straight line, left to right across the first nine holes of the golf course. As this was too near the castle, it was moved by the Lowther family to the position now occupied by the A174 and the tree belt planted to hide it from view.

Framed by the ornamental arch, the main entrance to the Castle.
The abundance of ivy, together with a similar covering on the rear of the building was later removed.

Probably taken in 1948, this is a group of the first ICI staff to work at the Castle

The Cleveland Hunt met regularly at the Castle during the early years. (1959)

The Coat of Arms was created in 1947 by L. H. F. Sanderson of ICI's Central Staff Office, following a chance conversation with the Chairman of Wilton, Dr. J.W. Armit.

Mr. Sanderson, a former private secretary to the Chairman of ICI, and for many years a student of heraldry, relished the task given him, and endeavoured to link any relevant historical associations together with an appropriate ICI background.

The underlying idea of the shield was to represent the six Divisions of ICI primarily concerned with Wilton's activities, whilst the supporters and the crest represent the local associations. Each section of the shield symbolises in its turn the activities and associations of its own Division.

Here is a brief description of each of the six so-called 'quarters' (clockwise from top left).

First Quarter - Billingham Division

Billingham's products and activities (hydrogen, nitrogen, coke, mining) are almost identical with the four 'elements' of Aristotle, viz; earth, air, fire and water. These are shown by the four signs used by medieval alchemists on a background of black, white, red and blue, also representing these elements. The yellow cross on a blue ground has long been associated with the city and cathedral of Durham.

Second Quarter- General Chemicals Division

The green and yellow background represents

chlorine and sulphur, two of the Division's main products. At the bottom of the shield is the heraldic form of a thunderbolt, the symbol for electricity, again very important to the Division, and the 'liver' or cormorant holding a branch of 'laver' or seaweed is a reference to the origins from which Liverpool (headquarters of the Division) draws its name.

Third Quarter - Dyestuffs Division

The red and white background signifies the Division's involvement with the textile industries of Lancashire and Yorkshire. The purple iris represents the original discovery of a purple dye by Perkin in 1856. This dye became the basis of the modern dyestuffs industry. The iris is 'charged' with a golden hexagonal benzene ring, symbolising chemical and technical achievements. The Lancaster and York roses refer to the two largest factories of the Division, Blackley and Huddersfield.

Fourth Quarter - Alkali Division

The blue background is a feature of the coat of arms of Lord Stanley of Alderley, former owner of Winnington Hall. The demi-lion and six-pointed stars are taken from the coats of arms of the Brunner and Mond families.

The wheatsheaf was in wide use throughout Cheshire and can be traced back to the first Earl of Chester in 1153.

The yellow lion is taken from the arms of Belgium as a tribute to the achievements and contribution of the Solvay family, whilst the blue and white wavy lines represent brine.

Fifth Quarter - Plastics Division

The primitive vases symbolise the earliest known efforts in the plastics arts, whilst the green and white background represents Welwyn Garden City, and the hart on the chevron indicates Hertfordshire.

Sixth Quarter - Explosives Division

The three windowed tower refers to the legend of St. Barbara, who in the middle ages was adopted as the patron saint of gunpowder makers. The blue and white background in the form of St. Andrews Cross recall the Scottish origins of the Division.

Other features of the Coat of Arms are: The small centre shield - 'Escutcheon of Pretence' consists of a silver dragon, to commemorate the Lowther family's association with the castle.

The border surrounding the shield represents the overall authority of ICI, the ermine suggesting the sovereignty, while the yellow 'bezants' (the heraldic symbol for money) indicate ICI's financial authority.

Over the shield is an esquire's helmet, on which is the crest consisting of a representation of the castle itself, bearing (in the tradition of punning heraldry), an arm holding a dagger as a tribute to Wilton's first Chairman - Dr. Armit. The supporter on the left is St. Cuthbert, to whom the small church at Wilton is dedicated, and the blue lion on the right represents a long standing association with the Debrus family, who in the twelfth century owned much property in Thornaby, and founded a priory where Middlesbrough now stands.

Finally the Latin motto - 'Not for ourselves, but for all', reflected both the interests for which Wilton was established, and the spirit with which it looked forward to the future.

The years between 1946 and 1960 were a period of great activity for both the chemical plants and the people who constructed and operated them.

The following selection of photographs attempts to illustrate those times.

Taken in August 1946, this is the first known construction photograph, showing the North-South Road, looking North at chainage 1300.

General site view, looking West from the Met. Station at Wilton Grange. *(1947)*
ICI had its own meteorological station, but forecasts were regularly received from R.A.F. Middleton-St-George (now Teesside Airport), particularly when strong winds and gales could affect scaffolding safety during construction.

A crane arriving at the North-South Road on transport vehicle No.3. *(1947)*

Looking North along the lane to Wilton Grange Farm in the heavy snow of March 1947.

Vessel for the I.P. (Intermediate Pressure) *Boiler being unloaded at the Dormanstown Area.* (1947)

Steelwork erection for the I.P. Boilerhouse. (1947)

Early excavation of the entrance shaft at Teesport for the first tunnel under the River Tees. (1947)

Transport vehicle No.1.
Commercial Lorry. (1947)

Transport vehicle No.2.
Scammell Horse. (1947)

Transport vehicle No.4.
Tipper Wagon. (1947)

The Labour-Medical Building under construction using the 'Smiths Building System' - an early method of prefabricated construction. (1947)

General view of the gantry used for the 'Smiths Building System'. (1947)

Interior of Main Stores. *(1948)*
Taken from the crane control cabin, in the N.E. corner, showing the rail tracks on the right.
The sitewide railway system was eventually taken out of service, and restricted to the
Northern end of the site and the Chlorine branch line.

Members of the Works Managers Committee pose informally on the lawns at the rear of the Castle. (1948)

Most of the steelwork erection is completed for No.1 Olefines Plant. (1949)

Construction of No.2 Process Office. (1949)

The I.P. Boilerhouse Control Room, with operator. (1949)

Construction of the Main Power Station, looking across Piccadilly Roundabout. (1949)
The I.P. (Intermediate Pressure) Boilerhouse can be seen on the right

Looking North from the top of the P.F. Building. (1949) The I.P. Boilerhouse is on the extreme left, and the open area in the foreground was later to be occupied by the Personnel/Medical Block and Site Management Offices.

A very busy time in the Main Stores. (1950)

Activity at the Upgang Borehole Site. *(1950)*
In the search for a satisfactory water supply, boreholes were sunk in many places. Above can be seen a typical drilling scene, together with two contractors and their rather attractive pick-up truck. The steam train in the background is on the Middlesbrough to Whitby line. A water supply from Worsall was eventually chosen.

The arrival of a column for No.1 Olefines Plant. *(1950)*

Looking South across Piccadilly Roundabout. *(1950)*
Early construction of the UF/WF Plant can be seen behind the pipe rack. The old look-out tower can still be seen on the Eston Hills. This was later demolished, and replaced by a solid monolith.

After the opening ceremony,
Dr. Armitt enjoys a game of
dominoes with fellow
Recreation Club members.

Dr. J.W. Armitt, Wilton Council Chairman, performing the opening ceremony of the Recreation Clubhouse.
(17th December, 1951)

Wilton's first ambulance, with driver, John Whyman outside the original Medical Centre. (1951)

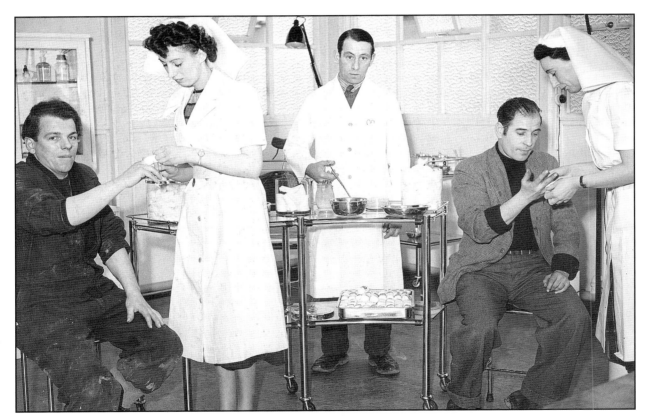

The Medical Centre Treatment Room. (1951)

No.1 Ethylene Oxide/Glycol Construction. *(1951)*
In the foreground is part of No.1 Polythene Plant. Top left are Trinity Offices with the original three buildings (hence the name). Lissapol N is to top right.

Early construction of the Chlorine Plant Cell Rooms - Bain Works. *(1951)*
On extreme left is the first signs of the Polythene Finishing Plant, and also shown are the incomplete Northway North, and South Roads. Note the expanse of fields in the background

The Grange Restaurant. *(1952)*
Seen as originally built, before the later extensions were added.
Note the bus stops on the right.

The kitchen staff are ready for action.

Staff from the Olefines Plant enjoying a dinner at Billingham. (1952)

Workers queueing for their pay at the first Personnel Block, located on the North East corner of Piccadilly Roundabout. (1952)

Many social functions were enjoyed during the early years. This is a selection from 1952.

An early Wilton Fire Crew. *(1953)*
Chief Shuttleworth is third from left.

The Post Girls of 1953.

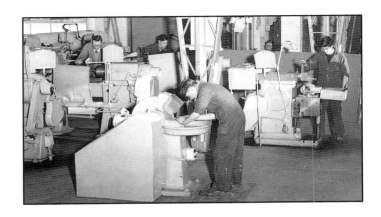

Interior views of the original Apprentice Training School. (1953)

Visitors being shown the site model. (1953)

Ladies taking the plunge at the 1953 swimming gala. *Note how near the spectators are.*

Celebrations following the winning of a football trophy. *(1953)*

The Tennis Section. *(1953)*

*Construction of a section of the Main Sewer.
(1954)*

The Titanium Plant under construction. *(1954)*
*In the background can be seen Olefines 1, part of the Polythene Plant, Lime Handling, and in the distance,
British Steel at Redcar.*

A social gathering at the Recreation Club. *(1954)*
Among those in the group are J.C.H. McEntee, A. Caress, J. Hughes, S. Comer,
C.F.R. Harrison and C.M. Wright

J. Hughes *(Wilton Council Technical Director)****, in action at the opening of the Recreation Club***
Bowling Green. *(1954)*
Among those watching are Bill Griffiths, Charlie Brown, Ron Wynn, Peter Dormand,
Rex Robinson and Doug Tonkin.

Wilton Foremans Association Dinner at the Coatham Hotel, Redcar. (1954)

Luxurious mess-room facilities. (1955)
You would almost expect to lift the stove up and reveal the entrance to a tunnel!

Group of ladies from Secretary's Department. *(1955)*
Joy Cope (secretary to Frank Potter) second left, and Nancy Blake (Registry) fourth right.

Darts competition at the Recreation Club. *(1955)*

ICI Wilton F.C.
Season 1954-55

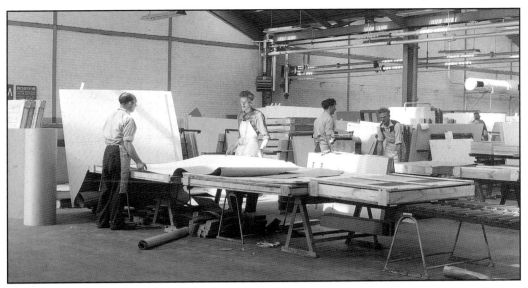

Packing finished sheets of Perspex prior to despatch. (1955)

Loading the 2000th ton of Polythene produced at Wilton. (1955)

Ladies in the Terylene Canteen serving hungry workers. (1955)

English Electric 350 HP Diesel Locomotive. *(1955)*

Group of Transport vehicles and drivers. *(1955)*

Interior of the Titanium Plant - Bain Works. *(1956)*
Showing the Sodium Handling and Reactor Area.

View of Bain Works, looking from the Power Station observation platform. *(1956)*
The two 'open' brine storage tanks on the South East corner of Piccadilly Roundabout were used in the production of Chlorine and Caustic Soda by electrolysis. In the background can be seen Terylene Works.

Construction work. *(1956)*

The crane erected for the construction of No.5 Boiler at the Power Station. *(1956)*

Dr Jenkin Evans digs the 'first sod' for the new Medical Centre. *(1956)*
Looking on are his secretary Mrs Booth, Sister Todd and two Wilton Medical Officers.

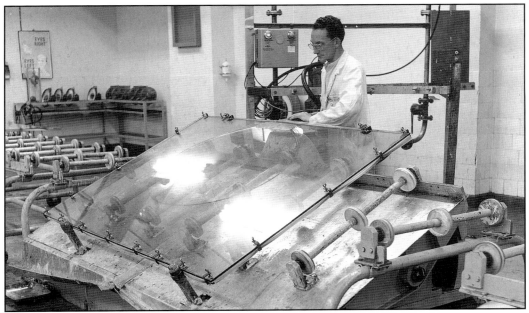

A pouring table - Perspex Production. *(1956)*
The liquid Perspex can clearly be seen spreading out between two sheets of glass. A rubber seal around the edges formed the flat mould for the sheet.

The site for the Water Treatment Plant. *(1956)*
In the background can be seen Nylon Works under construction.

Lansing Bagnall truck and trailer in Main Stores. *(1957)*

The South Road at rush hour. *(1957)*
The original track to Wilton Grange Farm went down the east side of the hedge, cut through a gate, and continued on the west side of the hedge. This 'kink' was maintained by ICI as they developed the road.

Installation of Butane to power passenger cars due to the Suez Crisis, and subsequent petrol shortage. *(1957)*

During 1957 a number of Open Days were organised.

Workers were invited to bring their families onto the site, and were transported around in a fleet of hired buses.

The convoy makes its way around Piccadilly Circus.

Families watching a demonstration in Central Workshops.

Arriving at Piccadilly Restaurant.

Enjoying afternoon tea at Piccadilly Restaurant.

Construction area for Nylon Works. *(1957)*
*The nitric acid absorption tower has just completed its journey from the Stockton works of
Ashmore, Benson Pease & Co.*

Terylene Works. *(1957)*
*Looking South East from the top of the UF/WF Plant. The Site Management Block was later added on to the
Personnel/Medical Centre in the right foreground.*

Post Girls and Boys at No. 2 Process Office. *(1957)*
*Although sorting of mail into pigeon holes has not changed much over
the years, the method of delivery certainly has.*

The 'Heavy Shop' of the Main Workshops. (1957)

Interior of a Cell Room on the Chlorine Plant. (1957)

Opening of the New Medical Centre. *(1957)*
Left to Right: R.A. Banks, ICI Personnel Director; J. McEntee, Chairman - Wilton Council;
Dr. Armor, ICI Chief Medical Officer; Dr. Jenkin Evans, Wilton Chief Medical Officer.

Medical Department Staff. *(1957)*
Photographed outside the original building just prior to the opening of the new Medical Centre.

Loading the first batch of Nylon Polymer produced at Wilton. (1957)

Part of the recently constructed Nylon Works. (1957)
Shows the original layout of the Main Offices.

The Nylon Works Acids Plant. *(1958)*
Looking North East.

The Polymer and Acids Plants of Nylon Works. *(1958)*
Looking North West from the recently opened Apprentice Training Centre.

Sir Ewart Smith unveiling the plaque to mark the opening of the new Apprentice Training Centre.
(30th April 1958)

Visitors to the Training Centre view the latest machining techniques. (1958)

Up-to-date classroom facilities in the Apprentice Training Centre. (1958)

A group of Bobbin Boys and management from the Terylene Plant. (1958)

Open Day Visitors to Terylene Works examining the Creel Bins. (1958)

The latest Terylene fashions on display in the Works Restaurant. (1958)

Plenty of tempting food on offer to the Terylene Open Day visitors. (1958)

The Chairman of the Works Council, Vic Goodsell, with models from a Terylene fashion show at the Castle. (1958)

The Site Model. (1958)
This was stored in the Castle cellars and set up on trestles in the ballroom when required.
It was kept up to date by Edgar Hansell, Castle Club Steward/Modelmaker.

The Water Treatment Plant. *(1958)*
Photographed just after completion.

The Butakon Plant. *(1958)*

Sir John Hunt *(on right)* ***visits Wilton Castle.*** *(1958)*
Sir John led the 1953 Royal Geographical Society Expedition to Everest when Hillary and Tenzing made the first successful final ascent.

The first edition of the Wilton News, hot off the press. *(1958)*
Among the onlookers are Vic Goodsell, Editor - Wilf Collinson, and Bill Cummings.

The Opening of the Wilton Golf Course. *(1958)*
Left to right; Hugh Laurie, (Wilton Professional), Henry Cotton, (Three times British Open Winner),
P.C. Allen. (ICI Deputy Chairman) and the Teesside Amateur Champion.
The course was originally only 9 holes. On the last green, opposite the Castle, Henry Cotton holed his
shot from about 50 yards!

Visit of the Archbishop of York, Michael Ramsey, *(later Archbishop of Canterbury). (1958)*
On left is Doug Thomson, Services Works with K.S. Jackson, Bain Works and Ossie Grenfell,
Reception Officer on right.

One of the first customers at the newly opened snack bar. (1959)

The Grange Restaurant butcher with a display of Christmas produce. (1958)

Hugh Gaitskell, *on left,* ***and John McEntee view the*** ***Power Station from Piccadilly Roundabout.*** *(1959)* *But for his sudden death in 1963, Mr Gaitskell, Leader of the Labour Party, would almost certainly have become Prime Minister instead of Harold Wilson.*

Mr Gaitskell chats informally to some of the Wilton Management.

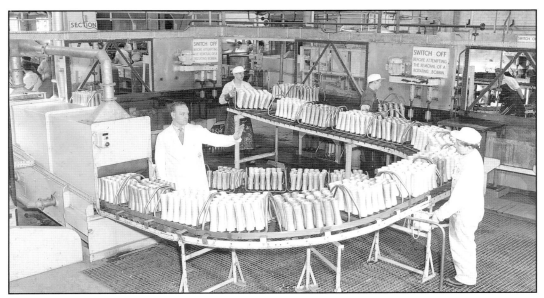

The Filament Yarn Section - Terylene Plant. *(1959)*
Shows the return of cleaned bobbins for re-use in the plant.

A fine group of Bobbin Boys. *(1959)*

Looking behind the Power Station, across the coal conveyor, and I.P. Boiler House. *(1959)*
In the centre can be seen the future site of the Aniline Plant.

Diners in the Grange Restaurant. (1959)

The battery of free piston gas generators, used for driving the compressors on No. 3 Olefines Plant.

The Gas Separation and Refrigeration Section of No. 3 Olefines Plant Control Room.
This later became the Control Room of the Ethylene Oxide Derivatives (EOD) Plant.

The recently commissioned No. 3 Olefines Plant. (1959)

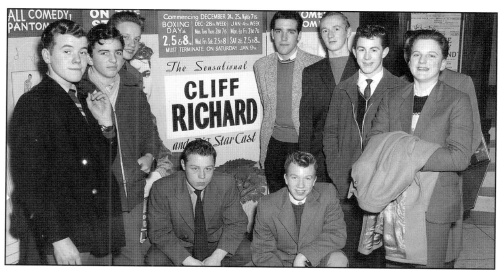

The Terylene Bobbin Boys Christmas Outing to the Globe Theatre, Stockton. (1960)

The Olefine Works Childrens Christmas Party. (1960)

Dai Rees, (centre) visits the Wilton Golf Club. (1960)

The New Mobile Snack Bar. (1960)

Looking North West across part of No. 3 Olefines Plant. *(1960)*
The four Trinity Offices, Paraxylene and Nos. 1 and 2 Olefines Plants can be seen.

The Propylene Oxide/Glycol Plant. *(1960)*

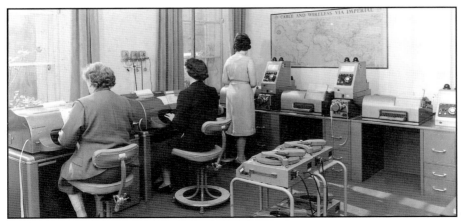

The Teleprinter Room in No. 2 Process Office. *(1960)*

Accounts Department. *(1960)*
Located in huts near the area now occupied by the T8 Plant.

The Main Workshops of the Apprentice Training School. *(1960)*

The Bagging Operation of Nylon Polymer Chip. *(1960)*
BNS stood for British Nylon Spinners, at the time an equal partnership between ICI and Courtaulds.

A load of Polymer Chip leaving the Nylon Warehouse. *(1960)*

The 'Propathene' Polypropylene Plant Compressor House. (1960)

An unusual display of safety posters, in front of Piccadilly Restaurant. (1960)

The ladies of the Keep Fit Class and their instructor, in the Recreation Club gymnasium. (1960)

The Keep Fit ladies in action! (1960)

With the major production plants well established, and an efficient service infrastructure in place, construction activity through the 1960's was mainly engaged in uprating the existing facilities to meet an ever increasing demand for product.

In 1963 No. 2 Paraxylene Plant was commissioned, between 1964 - 69 extensive uprating in the Power Station resulted in 5, 6, 7, 8 and 9 Boilers being brought into operation, and in 1966 No. 4 Olefines Plant was started-up.

The expansion of Nylon production, sanctioned in 1964, and known as Nylon Vll was also completed in 1966.

To ensure safe and efficient transport of ethylene, the 135 mile, Trans-Pennine Pipeline was completed in 1968, the same year as the Butadiene 2 Plant became operational.

In 1969 the No. 2 Ethylene Oxide and Ethylene Glycol Plants and No. 5 Olefines Plant were all commissioned.

Column being erected on No. 4 Olefines Plant. (1965)

No. 2 Paraxylene Plant. (1963)

The latest Terylene fashions come under close scrutiny. (1961)

Loading of Nylon Polymer, prior to transportation to B.N.S. Plants at Doncaster, Gloucester or Pontypool for spinning. (1961)

Diving display held at the Recreation Club as part of the Commonwealth Training Week. (1961)

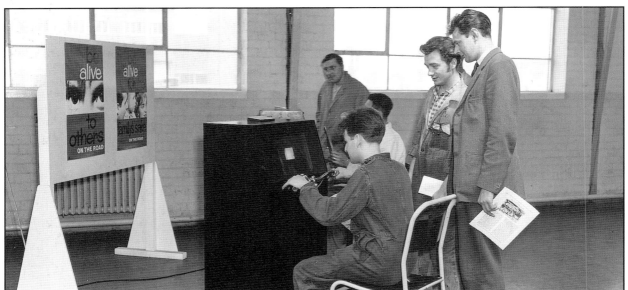

Using the latest technology, staff were encouraged to be aware of the need for road safety, as can be seen by this display in the Piccadilly Training Centre. (1961)

An open day visitor to the Analytical Labs tries her hand at glass blowing. (1961)

Visitors to Site Maintenance examine a very tidy tractor. (1961)

A Spinning Bank of the Terylene Plant. (1962)

Part of the Creel Bin Area on the Terylene Plant. (1962)

Group of Messenger Girls. *(1962)*
Charlie Brown, (Castle & Head Commissionaire in charge of messenger girls) in the centre,
with Bill Griffiths on left, and the Post Room Superintendent on the right.

The Transport Offices and Workshops area. *(1962)*

Another significant royal occasion occured in April 1962, when HRH Princess Margaret arrived at Wilton.

After inspecting the Nylon Solvents Control Room she drove through the site to visit the Terylene and Perspex Plants, before taking tea at the Grange Restaurant.

HRH Princess Margaret arriving at Nylon Works.

Mr. Banks, *(Main Board Director) accompanies Her Royal Highness into the Grange Restaurant.*

The waiting onlookers outside Nylon Main Offices.

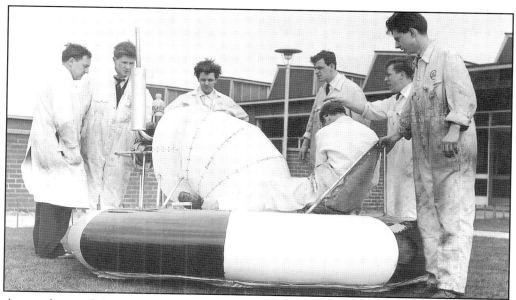

Apprentices and their instructors testing out a hovercraft built at the Training Centre. (1962)

Recreation Club members enjoying a drink with local actress, June Laverick. (1962)
Miss Laverick, (seated on right) was groomed for stardom by the Rank charm school of the fifties, and appeared in films such as Doctor at Large in 1956 and Son of Robin Hood in 1958.

Fire Awareness Demonstration. (1963)

View from Nylon Polymer, looking across Thorntree Restaurant towards the Water Treatment Plant. (1963)

Bain Works, looking from the top of the UF/WF Plant across Queens Avenue. (1963)

Vehicle Maintenance in Transport Workshops. (1964)

Ronnie Hilton and his musicians at the Recreation Club. *(1964)*
Vocalist Ronnie, (on right), made a number of successful recordings in the late 50's and early 60's. His last record, Windmill in Old Amsterdam, was a hit in 1965.

Ivor Emanuel sings at the Recreation Club, accompanied by members of the Wilton Male Voice Choir. *(1964)*

This 'Showbiz' XI Football Team played at the Recreation Club. *(1965)*
A very young Des O' Connor can be seen in the centre, with Dave King crouched in front of him.

Viscount Slim *(centre)* **with T.B. Clark** *(left)* **and K.W. Palmer** *(right)* **at Wilton Castle.** *(1965)*
Viscount Slim led the 14th Army in the victories of 1944-45, driving the Japanese out of Burma.
After seven years as Governor General of Australia he joined the ICI Main Board.

Over the years, many different vehicles have been used on the Wilton Site.
These pages show a selection from the 1960's.

Terylene delivery vehicle. (1961)

Post Bus. (1962)

Despite a few alterations to its appearance, this 1947 Scammell was still in use as a 'site only' vehicle in 1964

Harry Wheatcroft, well known rose expert offers advice during his visit to the Recreation Club. (1965)

Danny Blanchflower, former captain of Spurs and Northern Ireland international footballer, interviewed ex-Middlesbrough star, Wilf Mannion for the BBC TV Sportsview programme. (1965)

Danny Blanchflower autographed a teacup as a memento of his visit.

The Vinyl Acetate Plant. *(1965)*
This was situated in the extreme north east corner of the Olefines North area.

This 90 ton Mark 9 Centurian tank, lent by the Queen's Own Hussars, was the centrepiece of a 1966 Nylon Works safety campaign, until an unknown ex-Armoured Corps driver was tempted to take it for a little spin!

The 'Swinging Sixties' were very much on display at this Wilton fashion show. (1966)

David Attenborough, (second from right) chats informally during his visit to Wilton. (1966)

Printing Section, in No. 1 Process Offices. (1966)

Part of Nylon Works, looking South East from the Solvents Area. (1966)
Shows the final stages of construction on Inters II, ADN Crude, HMD and Acids II

Computer Control Console - No. 4 Olefines Plant. *(1967)*
The 200,000 tpa plant could be started or stopped by pressing one switch on this console.
Without a computer, the operator would have to manually adjust 45 controls.

No. 4 Olefines Plant. (1967)

Construction is well advanced on No. 5 Olefines Plant (above),
whilst the demolition of the No. 1 Plant is shown below. (1967)

The apprentices were always encouraged to keep fit. (1968)

Fashion conscious Nylon office staff wearing the new shorter dress lengths. (1968)

Looking East across Davies Works. *(1968)*
Terylene Works is in the centre, with No. 5 Olefines and Ethylene Oxide at the top.

Looking towards the North East area of the site. *(1968)*
Showing the original coal conveyor route to the Power Station, and Olefines and Polythene Works.

Nos 3 and 4 Olefines Plants.
(1968)
Polythene 5 Plant is in the top left corner.

The Propathene Offices, and Nos 1 and 2 Plants. *(1968)*
The T.P.X. (Transport Plastic Experimental) Plant is towards the top centre.

Control Room of the Propathene No. 2 Plant. (1968)

The start-up of No. 5 Olefines Plant. (1969)

Restaurant prices had to be adjusted with the advent of decimalisation. (1971)

Training session to prepare staff for the conversion to decimalisation. (1971)

Coal Board Chairman, Lord Robens visited the Power Station. *(1971)*

The last wagon load of coal being tipped into the Power Station conveyor system. *(1971)*
The station was converted to burn various by-product gases and oils until the reversion to coal of Nos. 5 and 6 boilers in 1985.

The T6 Terephthalic Acid Plant. *(1972)*

The T7 Terephthalic Acid Plant. *(1973)*

One of the Wilton Firecrews with their equipment. *(1973)*
In the background is the Employment Office section of No. 1 Process Offices, and the Polythene Offices and Plants.

The Aniline Plant. *(1973)*

The Wilton telephonists in the No. 2 Process Office exchange. (1973)

Looking East from the Power Station observation platform, towards the Polythene Plants. *(1973)*
The Propathene Plants are top right, and Olefines 4 is top left

The Paraxylene 5 Plant. *(1974)*

A very attractive group of ladies from Supply Department. (1974)

The Plastics Distribution Office. (1974)

In 1974, Jim Cox of Petrochemicals Division, wrote an article for the ICI Magazine, describing remnants of war-time defences still on the Wilton Site.
The concrete posts, pictured below with Jim, were two of many, positioned to prevent a potential invader from landing aeroplanes and gliders on flat farmland areas of the North East coast.
The building above, was the remains of a small camp to house airmen, when an area on the North West side of Wilton was used as a dummy airfield, complete with exact wooden replicas of fighter planes.

Jack Charlton (*then Manager of Middlesbrough FC*), **visited the Training Centre to promote road safety.** (*1975*)

Aerial view of the Olefines 6 construction site, showing the basic layout of the plant. (*1975*)
The Wilton Centre, in its original form, with no Semi-Tech, can be seen in the background.

The summer of 1976 was memorably hot!
These ladies from No. 2 PO found time to soak up the sun in the courtyard.

The rush hour traffic at the West Gate was always particularly heavy. *(1976)*

Some of the workforce present at the closure of the DMT South Plant, Davies Works. *(1976)*
By 1983, the building would be converted to produce Melinar PET, used in the manufacture of plastic bottles.

Nylon Works. *(1977)*
*Showing early stages of
construction of the new
cooling tower.*

The Olefines 6 Plant begins to take shape. *(1977)*
*This also shows extensions to Ethylene Oxide (top left), construction of storage tanks and maintenance
depot (top centre), with Sandpits Farm still remaining (top right).*

Control Room of the Propathene No. 3 Plant. *(1977)*

The recently completed, second tunnel under the River Tees. *(1977)*

Moss Evans, General Secretary Designate of the Transport & General Workers Union (3rd from right), made a brief introductory visit to Wilton. He is pictured chatting informally to site union officials. (1977)

Members of Middlesbrough FC visited the Wilton Centre. (1977)
In the centre are (from 4th left) Harold Shepherdson, Stewart Boam, Billy Ashcroft, Willie Maddren and the manager, John Neal.

Dr Rab Telfer, *(Petrochemicals Division Chairman)****, welcomes the Chairman of the Coal Board, Sir Derek Ezra to the Apprentice Training Centre.*** *(1978)*

The Ethylene Oxide 2 Plant. *(1978)*

These 'smoke signals' seen against the construction of the Butadiene 3 columns, issued from a flare stack on the Olefines North area. (1979)

Dr Jim Whiston with his Olefines 6 start-up management team. (1979)

In 1979, using modules prefabricated by the No. 1 Task Force, the TA Pilot Plant was transported from Middleway, and erected in an area adjacent to the Davies Works offices.

A 'fully dressed' column, prefabricated in Holland for the TA T8 Plant, arrives on site. (1979)

Arthur Lowe visited Wilton, whilst appearing at the Billingham Forum in 1979.

The actor, best known for his role as Captain Mainwaring in Dad's Army, was pictured with his actress wife, Joan, receiving a memento from Brian Coldwell.

Many of the Olefines 6 workforce involved in the plant start-up assembled for this photograph. (1979)

On Sunday October 7th 1979, the demolition took place on Nylon Works of a redundant cooling tower.
Process Supervisor, Bill Crosby won the raffle that gave him the prize of turning the switch to detonate the explosives.

The 'fully dressed' reaction column being lifted into position on the Propathene 5 Plant. (1979)

Aerial view of the Ethylene Oxide 2 Plant. (1979)

Aerial photograph of the Olefines 6 Plant during start-up (above),
and (below) *a much more tranquil view of the plant at dusk.* (1979)

The massive construction programme of the late 1970's was successfully concluded in the early 1980's with the coming on-stream of the T8 Pure Terephthalic Acid Plant, the Ethylene Dichloride (EDC) Plant, the Chlorine Plant, Ethoxylates 4, Ethylene Oxide Derivatives (EOD) and the No.5 Propathene Plant.

Such levels of simultaneous capital expenditure would not be seen at Wilton again, and over the next few years major construction would be limited to the adaptation of existing buildings for the first Melinar Plants, and the reversion of 5 and 6 boilers to coal burning in the Power Station.

In 1982, BP Chemicals agreed with ICI to take over the ownership of the Polythene business, an arrangement which would ultimately turn out to be the forerunner of a great many other divestments in the coming years.

The opening in 1984 of the Wilton Technical Centre heralded a period of substantial activity in Research and Technology with many innovative new materials being developed.

Aerial view of the Wilton Centre. *(1980)*
The first Semi-Tech buildings are on the right, just in front of the remains of Town Farm, with the recently commissioned Olefines 6 Plant behind.

The almost completed EDC Plant.
(1980)
Originally intended to produce VCM (Vinyl Chloride Monomer), a change in business strategy during construction resulted in much of the planned plant never being completed.

The Propathene 5 Plant under construction. *(1980)*
Utilising new technology, tested in the Gas Phase Pilot Plant built near the site of the redundant Butakon Plant, this would supercede the exisiting Propathene Plants.

ICI was an active participant in the Youth Opportunities Programme created by the Government in the late 1970's.

YOPs as they were known, worked mainly in offices throughout the site, some gaining full-time employment at the end of their placement.

This photograph shows a 1980 intake of school leavers including the 1000th trainee at Wilton, **Julie Carter of Ormesby** *(Third row from front, on right).*

Christmas Dinner for the Catering Staff at Oaktree Restaurant. *(1980)*

As joint owners of Olefines 6, the Board of BP Chemicals visited the plant. *(1980)*
*Dr Rab Telfer (Petrochemicals Division Chairman), on left
and Dr Jim Whiston (Olefine Works Manager) on right.*

Some of the workforce involved in the final operations
of the Lime Handling Plant. (1980)

Looking from the roof of the Titanium Plant, towards Plastics Works Offices and the Propathene Plants. (1980)
Part of the construction of the Chlorine Plant can be seen in the foreground.

In September 1980, these workers assembled for the final shutdown of the first Chlorine Plant.
The commissioning of the new plant (below) *made the old technology redundant.*

Using a revolutionary method of construction, the Terephthalic Acid - T8 Plant begins to take shape. (1980)
Much of the plant was fabricated off-site. The photograph on the right shows the German-made compressor arriving at Tees Dock, whilst far right can be seen a small module being lifted into position.

The TA T8 Plant. (1981)

Using modular construction techniques, the Ethylene Oxide 2 Plant was uprated in 1981.

These workers were involved in production of the final batch of Titanium prior to the closure and demolition of the plant. (1982)

The road roller 'Astonisher' restored in No. 5 Depot prepares to return to Beamish Museum. *(1984)*

Using a local workforce, the ICI sponsored, Manpower Services Commission (MSC) training scheme was also responsible for the restoration of many other on-going projects, including the Mann's steam wagon, pictured at bottom of page upon completion in 1990, and the KI steam locomotive. (below).

The Wilton Technical Centre was opened in 1984 by Sir John Harvey-Jones, Chairman of ICI.

Sir John is seen here in the Materials Testing Laboratory (on right), **and** *(below) viewing the New Science Group display.*

The centre provided vital support in Research & Technology for many of ICI's businesses serving world-wide high-technology industries.

Plastics processing in the newly opened Semi-Tech Machinery Hall. (1984)

In the summer of 1985, a series of 'open days' allowed families and friends of the workforce to experience different aspects of the Wilton Site. A selection is shown on these two pages.

The Propathene 5 Plant Control Room

In the Wilton Centre, a display of the latest desk top computers was very popular.

The Main Power Station Control Room

Nylon Main Offices

Melinar Plant Offices

Olefines 6 Control Room

On a wet day in 1985, Sir Harry Secombe visited Wilton Castle to film a sequence for the ITV Highway programme. He is pictured (left) chatting to Rev. Peter Langford, the Wilton Industrial Chaplain.

Marking the achievement of One Million Hours worked on the Wilton Site without a Lost Time Accident, Bob Thomson, Deputy Site Manager presented a cheque for £5000 to the Wilton Healthcare Fund. (1986)
The cheque, accepted on behalf of the fund by Jim McAvoy, was later donated to the British Diabetic Association, Retinal Eye Camera Appeal.

Following its closure a few years earlier, the Lime Handling Plant, located on Boundary Road North, was demolished in 1986.

The plant (pictured on right in 1951) originally produced a slurry from the lime brought in from Buxton, to be used in the Propylene Oxide Plant.

The explosion was detonated by a carefully selected junior demolition 'expert'. (pictured below)

Two famous steam locomotives arrived at Wilton in 1986. The Blue Peter, *(top right)*, would be fully restored in a joint scheme involving the workforce at No. 5 Depot and members of the North Eastern Locomotive Preservation Group.

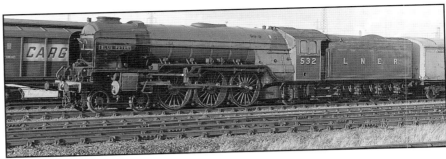

The Bittern, *(bottom right)*, cosmetically restored and renamed Silver Link would be placed on display at the National Railway Museum in York.

Another successful restoration from No. 5 Depot, the 69023 Joem being tested before transportation to the North York Moors Railway. *(1987)*
Joem had previously featured in a TV version of the Railway Children.

As part of an on-going link with the BBC TV programme Blue Peter, presenter Mark Curry checks progress with ICI's Ken Thompson. *(1987)*

HRH Prince Charles visited Wilton Castle in 1987 to launch the Cleveland Youth Business Centre, one of several, set up to provide practical support and guidance for young people.

Whilst at the Castle he took time out to sign the visitors book, and also to meet crowds of well-wishers gathered outside.

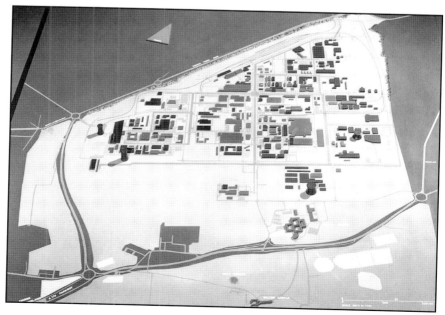

The Site Model. *(1987)*
The development of Wilton can clearly be seen in a comparison with the 1958 version shown on page 70.

In 1988, at the ceremony marking the official completion of the Power Station coal reversion project, Jim Miller, of ICI's Engineering Dept. was presented with this prize as winner of a competition to name a diesel locomotive.

The locomotive with the winning name, 'Wilton Coalpower' and it's consignment of coal was welcomed to Wilton by Jim, and the Chairmen of British Coal, ICI and British Rail.

An aerial view of the Propathene 5 Plant. (1988)

HM King Karl XVI Gustav of Sweden visited the Wilton Technical Centre in 1989, and in addition to viewing many laboratory displays, he unveiled a plaque to commemorate the installation of the ICI - SCIENTA IS300 Spectrometer, a pioneering Anglo-Swedish development.

Some people at Wilton would go to almost any lengths to collect for the Children in Need charity appeal. (1989)

Some of the Polyester Intermediates & Esters workforce gathered in front of the T7 Plant to celebrate One Million LTA Free Hours, achieved over a 21 month period. (1989)

To increase the efficiency of rail transport to and from the region, the Cleveland Freightliner Terminal was relocated from Portrack to a purpose built facility in the north west corner of the Wilton Site.

Direct access from the Trunk Road enabled companies from all over the area, as well as the Wilton Site to utilise the rail network.

The Rt Hon Paul Channon MP, (second from right), Secretary of State for Transport at the time, opened the terminal in 1989.

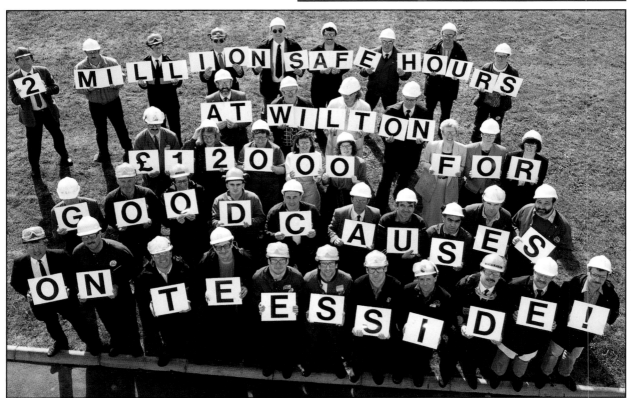

Early in April 1990, the Site achieved 2 million hours without a Lost Time Accident, the first time since site-wide records began. To mark the occasion a representative group of the workforce assembled for this photograph.

To encourage and maintain safety awareness throughout the site, the 'Big Quiz' had been held annually since 1989.

Fierce competition and inter-team rivalry resulted in a very entertaining and informative evening at the Recreation Club.

The 1991 winners, 'XARAC' from the Paraxylene Plant are presented with the trophy by Dr. Jim Carrick, Site Operations Manager. (below)

Sandy Anderson, (Teesside Operations Manager) **with the ICI Community Action team.** (1991)

Set up to provide practical help for local good causes, ranging from painting community halls to fitting smoke alarms in the homes of Teesside Pensioners.

The group harnessed the skills and enthusiasm of apprentices working within the Teesside Training and Enterprise scheme.

In December 1991, following five years of restoration in No. 5 Depot, the steam locomotive 60532 - Blue Peter was finally ready for the renaming ceremony.

Continuing the interest shown by the BBC throughout the restoration scheme, the honours fell to presenter Diane-Louise Jordan to unveil the nameplate. (Pictured right with Sandy Anderson and Norman Banning).

The recorder group (below) entertained the assembled guests, and were particularly impressive with their rendition of the Blue Peter signature tune.

In the 1990's many projects were undertaken to increase the flora and fauna on the Wilton Site. A number of ponds and nesting areas were provided to encourage wildlife.

This wildflower meadow in front of the Olefines 6 Plant was one of several planted in various areas around the site. (1992)

Situated to the South of Nylon Works, adjacent to Greystone Road, construction was well advanced for Enron's Teesside Power Station. (1992)

Another BBC TV presenter visited Wilton, this time, in 1993, Anthea Turner was at Wilton Castle to launch the Teesside Plastics Recycling Scheme.

A number of local schoolchildren were invited to help out, and as was usually the case, refreshments were provided.

Once again food was available, as these children discovered on an educational visit to the Wilton Centre.

After its launch in 1993, the Primary Science Caravan quickly became a popular visitor to local schools.

Using a series of practical, hands-on experiments, comparatively young children were able to discover the wonders of commercially based industrial science.

At the opening ceremony, Bill Perfitt, *Community Relations Manager,* **explained the benefits of the caravan to the invited guests.**

The ICI Community Relations display bus visited many events on Teesside, helping to create a more informed relationship between ICI and the local community.

ICI staff were able to participate with local organisers.

Many local organisations were able to benefit from substantial donations.

Through their entries for the Community Calendar competition, local schoolchildren increased awareness of the need to develop a better environment.
1995 winner Naomi Callum, (pictured above) *with Middlesbrough footballers, Craig Hignett and Paul Wilkinson.*

In 1995, the Olefines Production Area was granted 'Investor in People' status by the Teesside Training and Enterprise Council.

Brian Robson, Manager of Middlesbrough FC presented a commemorative plaque, and was photographed with some of the workforce involved.

Dr Mo Mowlam (MP for Redcar), **and Services Manager, George Ritchie at the opening of the Major Emergency Control Centre in 1995.**
From here, highly-skilled, trained professionals can manage emergencies at the Wilton International, Billingham or North Tees Sites.

Mike Gardner, CEO, ICI Petrochemicals (sixth from left), presented a joint ICI/Teesside Chemical Initiative (TCI) donation of £2000 to local schools, marking the winning by ICI of the TCI 'Community Chemical Company of the Year Award 1998'.

A Dynamic New Era Dawns in Wilton's Wonderful History

The chemical industry worldwide went through a period of massive change as the 1990's unfolded, with the industry across Teesside, and Wilton in particular, very much to the forefront of this quite dramatic trend.

Throughout almost all of the 1990's ICI businesses on Teesside have gone through a period of radical re-structuring bringing about major changes in the organisational portfolio. This has completely changed the ownership profile of Wilton - renamed 'Wilton International' in 1999 - as it heads confidently and positively towards the new Millennium and beyond.

To illustrate the breathtaking amount of change which has taken place at Wilton, particularly since 1993, it is worthwhile recapping on the major events which have unfolded in ICI since the mid 1990's.

In 1993, probably the most fundamental structural change in ICI's long history took place when the Company literally split itself into two separate entities - the Zeneca group of pharmaceutical, biological and agrochemical businesses and the traditional ICI bulk commodity chemical operations, many of them centred on Teesside, and Merseyside in the North West of England.

Although the impact of the 'Zeneca De-merger' on Teesside was relatively limited, the move signalled the start of a very active period of fundamental re-structuring throughout ICI, as the Company's new strategy moved away from heavy, bulk chemicals and more towards lighter, speciality products.

Much of this change has impacted directly on the Wilton International Site. But, despite coming as something of a cultural shock in the early stages, it is now being viewed positively as an evolutionary process which is diversifying Wilton's industrial base with a new crop of world class international chemical companies, each starting to harvest a rich mixture of new investment, new plants and businesses that they are committed to develop and grow.

1993 July 1st was a watershed date in Wilton's renaissance as it heralded the first really major business divestment by ICI to another company. The sale of the Nylon business to the American company DuPont, secured and transferred about 800 jobs, mainly at Wilton.

DuPont Chairman, Edgar S Woolard Jr, unveiled the plaque marking the transfer of Nylon Works to DuPont

1994 ICI's European polypropylene operations sold to the German firm, BASF (340 jobs at Wilton transferred). This business has since been renamed 'Targor' following a BASF joint venture with Hoechst.

Also, some 470 ICI Central Engineering staff were transferred to Redpath Engineering Services (UK).

1995 ICI sells the Ethylene Oxide and Derivatives to Union Carbide with 90 jobs secured at Wilton.

1996 ICI outsources the management of mainframe computing activities to Origin (53 Teesside jobs), and later in the year transferred to IBM around 45 people involved in IT, switchboard, and infrastructure services.

1997 ICI sells its UK Fertilizer business to Terra Industries Inc. of the USA (around 370 employees based at Wilton and Billingham).

In July the sale was announced of the Polyester and Films businesses to DuPont, involving the transfer of a total of almost 850 people at Wilton.

To mark the transfer of the Polyester business, the DuPont flag is raised outside Davies Offices.

1998 ICI completed the sale of the Amines and Derivatives business to Air Products, USA (125 jobs, some at Wilton but most at Billingham).

Also, on December 31st, ICI completed the sale of the Teesside Utilities and Services Business to the Enron Corp, of the USA for £300 million, with 560 ICI employees transferring to Enron as part of the agreement. Most of these were Wilton based, but a small number were from Billingham and North Tees Works.

1999 The Wilton Centre Headquarters building is sold to London property group, Threadneedle with about 40 jobs transferred.

On July 1st, ownership of several of ICI's major petrochemicals businesses, along with the Tioxide and Polyurethanes operations was transferred to the privately owned American company, Huntsman. This massive deal involved around 1,700 ICI employees, almost half based at Wilton, transferring their employment to Huntsman.

Jon Huntsman Sr., with sons Peter and Jon Jr. join their colleagues and ICI Managers for this photograph outside Wilton Castle.

On July 9th, another major new milestone in Wilton's ever changing history occurred with the unveiling of a plaque by Mo Mowlam, MP, Secretary of State for Northern Ireland, (pictured below) revealing the new logo for 'Wilton International'.

The new image and branding of the Site is represented by the logo depicting two industrious figures, building the 'W' of Wilton, signifying the dawn of a bright new era of hope for the future of the Site.

Whilst many people, particularly past ICI employees, are saddened by the massive changes which have taken place within ICI, more and more are coming to realise that re-structuring was inevitable, and the resulting broadening of Teesside's industrial base is vital to the future well-being of the Site.

It should be remembered that originally, Wilton comprised many different independent Divisions, albeit owned by ICI, each responsible for constructing and operating their own plants, whilst sharing services, feedstocks and resources.

The various divestments by ICI in the 1990's have almost brought things round full circle. Now, 50 years on, the Site is made up of a variety of independent major worldwide companies, each operating their own plants, and still sharing services, feedstocks and resources.

However, the strengths of Wilton will remain in its workforce, who, over the last 50 years have played a vital part in what must still be a virtually unique chemical production complex.

This final selection of photographs serves to illustrate much of the Wilton International Site as it prepares for the new Millennium.

Since purchasing ICI's European Nylon business with a £235 million deal in 1993, DuPont has invested heavily in its facilities at Wilton, making the raw materials which go into a vast array of modern products from carpets and sports clothing to delicate lingerie.

The Wilton Power Station. *Owned by Enron Teesside Operations Ltd since 1999 and a major contributor to the steam and electricity requirements of the site, using oil, gas and coal feedstocks.*

The E-One Fire Engine. *Widely acknowledged as one of the finest pieces of fire fighting equipment in the world. Owned by Enron Teesside Operations Ltd, American built E-One can project almost 30 tonnes of foam a minute onto a target.*

The Aniline Plant.
More than £70 million was spent by ICI in 1997 extending the existing Aniline Plant, (pictured) and constructing the entirely new Nitrobenzene Plant.

Nitrobenzene is a key raw material of aniline, which helps make polyurethane products used in footwear and insulation, among others. The new plant removed the need to transport the material from West Yorkshire, saving five million tanker miles per year.

Both plants were bought by Huntsman, in the summer of 1999.

The Melinar 5 Plant. Opened in 1996 and capable of producing 120,000 tonnes per year of polyethene terephthalate (PET), used in bottle plastic and other packaging. Owned and operated by DuPont since 1998.

BP Polyethylene Plant.

BP took over operational responsibility of the Polyethylene Plant at Wilton in 1996. The facilities had previously been operated by ICI on BP's behalf since 1982.

The plant has the capacity to manufacture around 90,000 tonnes of product per year.

The Novolen Plant.
Manufactures polypropylene and was originally bought from ICI by BASF in 1994.

Following a joint venture between BASF and Hoechst, the plant is now operated by Targor.

The Wilton Centre.
Now owned by Threadneedle Property Fund, the building currently houses around 2,000 people belonging to various companies, in approximately 500,000 sq. ft. of office and laboratory space.

This hydrogen production plant, commissioned in 1997, is operated by Air Products on behalf of fellow American company, DuPont.

The Ethylene Oxide Plant.
Owned by Union Carbide, the plant has a capacity to manufacture 300,000 tonnes per year of Ethylene Oxide.

Wilton International is today a world class multi-company manufacturing site, which welcomes chemical and other high energy process operations. The site offers a superb infrastructure and an extensive range of professional support services.

The new Wilton International 'Welcome Signs' erected at the gatehouses during 1999.

The Teesside Power Station.
Owned by Enron Corp. and four regional electricity companies, this 1875 Megawatt power station came into operation in 1993.

The SMP Plant, part of the recently-formed ICI Uniqema business at Wilton International.

The Nitrobenzene Plant.
Built in 1997, and bought from ICI by Huntsman in 1999.

The last three ICI Teesside Operations General Managers -
(left to right) **Sandy Anderson, Arthur Dicken, Bob Wasson**

Pictured in September 1999, the Site Directors of the various major international chemical companies operating
on the Wilton International Site, from left: Donald Austin (BP Amoco), Luis Batiz (Union Carbide),
Matthew Scrimshaw (Enron Teesside Operations Ltd), Kevin Ninow (Huntsman), Walter Burns (DuPont) and
Bob Wasson (ICI).

A sign of the changing times!
The new Wilton International Site sign, showing the range of
well-known international company names now based at Wilton.

Here's to the next 50 years of prosperity and

genuine hope for the preservation of the proud

heritage of chemicals and industrial manufacturing,

together with utilities and services provision at

Wilton, and the wider Teesside region.